Going to school

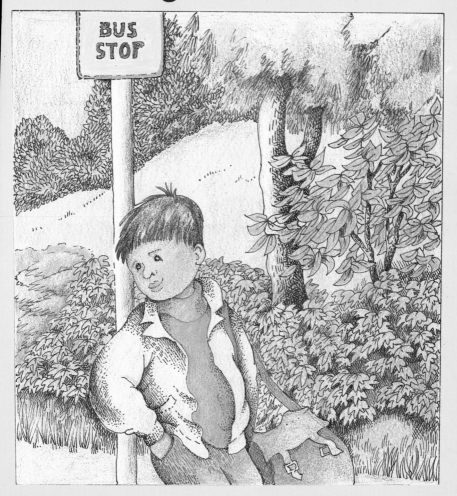

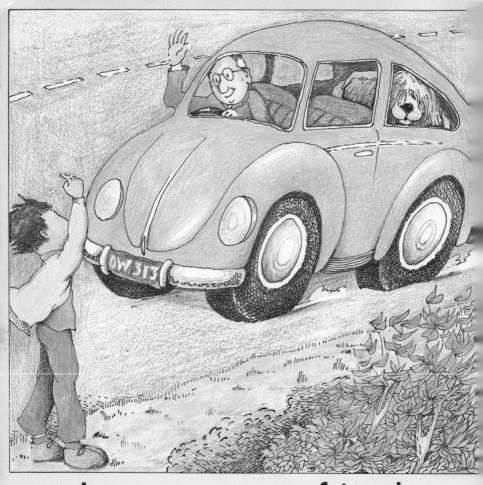

I wave to my friend,
the car driver.

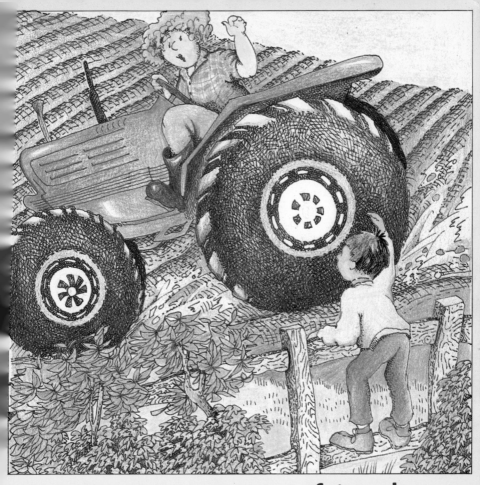

I wave to my friend,
the tractor driver.

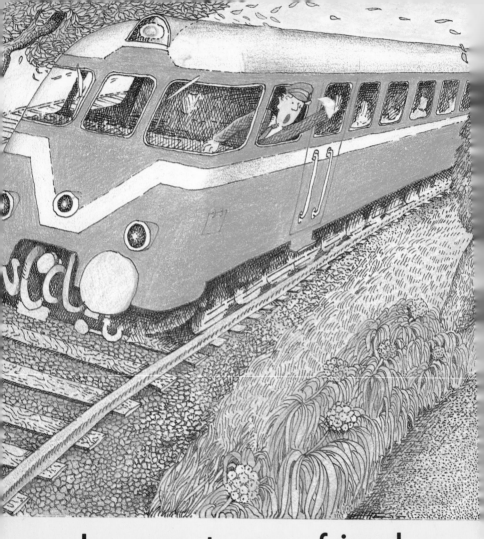

I wave to my friend,

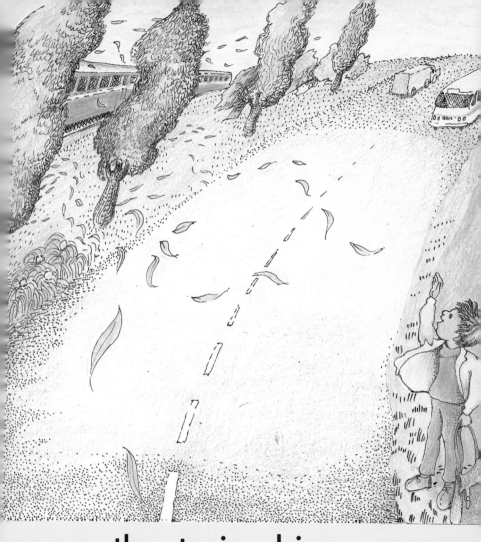

the train driver.

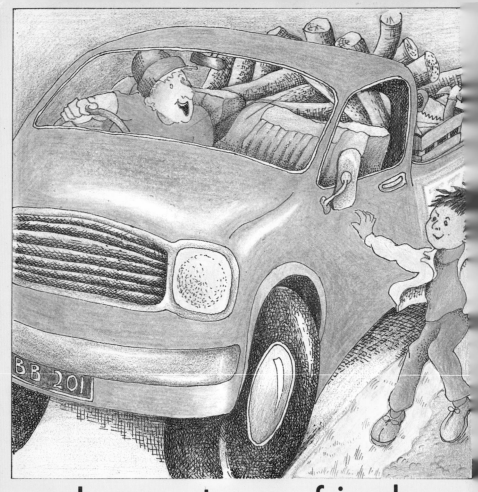

I wave to my friend,
the truck driver.

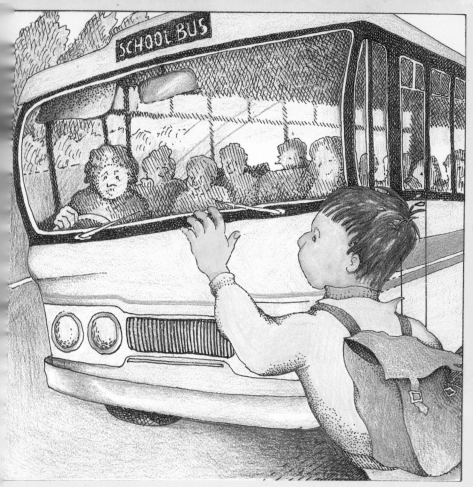

I wave to my friend,
the bus driver.

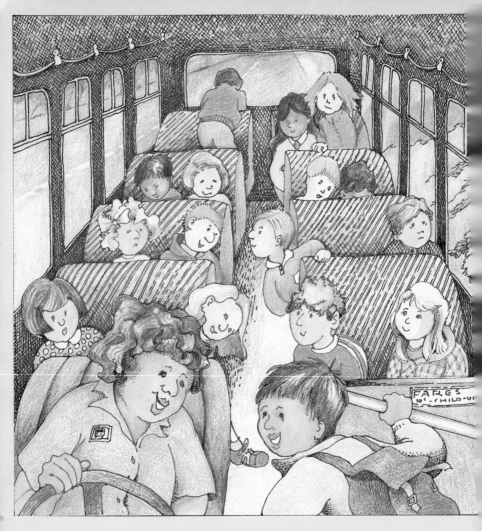

She's my Mum.